Mrs Noah's RAINY DAY Book

SUE ATKINSON
Illustrations by
SUSIE POOLE

Dear Reader,

I expect you've heard all about the adventure Noah and I had on the ark. Lots of people know the Bible story but not everyone knows what it was like for me. You can read my story in this book.

At first we had plenty to do looking after the animals, but then it became boring for everyone. It rained day after day. So as well as writing down my adventures I made up some things for you to do on rainy days. I hope you enjoy them.

Remember to keep a look out for rainbows. They remind us that God promises to look after us always.

With love from,

Mrs Noah

A LION BOOK

MAKE A FLIP BOOK

YOU NEED:

30 pieces of paper about 10x4cm
crayons
a paper fastener or string

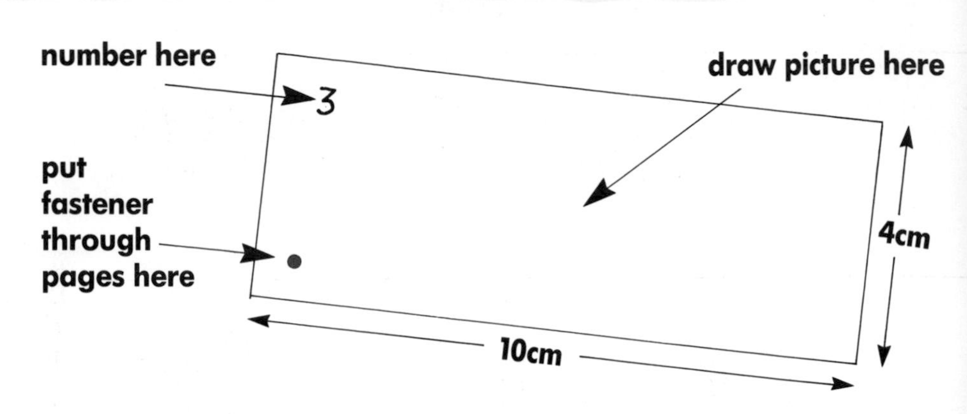

1 Make up a 'moving' story. You could show Mr Noah sawing wood, or a cat chasing a mouse.

2 Draw and number each picture in sequence. You need about 30 pictures altogether.

3 Put the pictures in order. But first decide which way you are going to 'flip' your book . . . otherwise your dove (see next page) might look as if it is flying backwards!

4 Fix the papers together in one corner. You can use tape, a paper fastener, or punch holes and use string.

5 Hold the book on the left and flip through the pages. The pictures will seem to move!

Why not draw Noah making the ark? On the right there are four pictures to get you started. They are pictures 1, 10, 20 and 30 . . . you have to draw the in-between ones.

On the next page there are 30 pictures of a dove flying for you to photocopy or cut out. Join at the dot and flip them starting from picture 1.

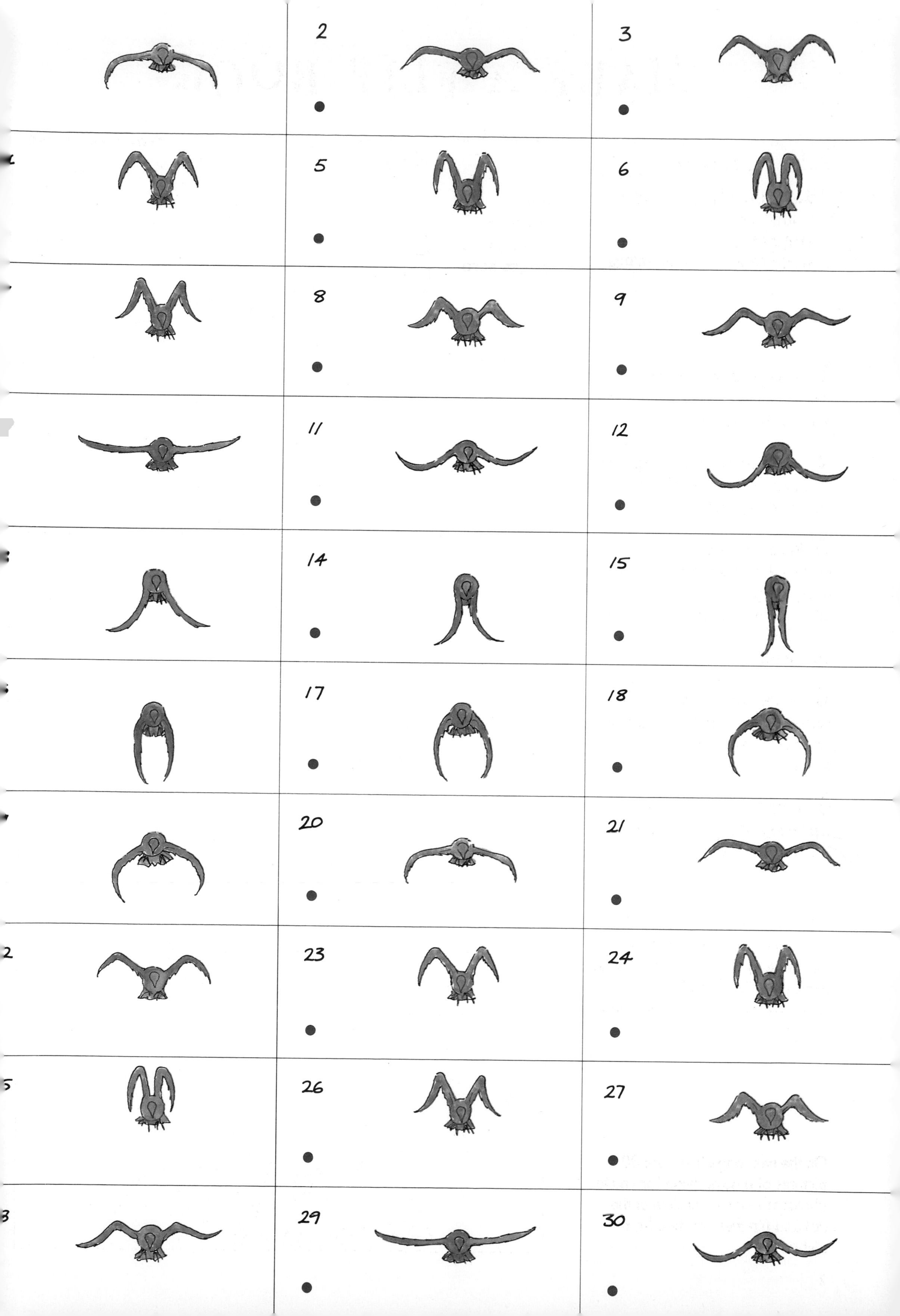
2
3
5
6
8
9
11
12
14
15
17
18
20
21
23
24
26
27
29
30

If you know the Bible story about Noah and the Flood, this retelling may give you a few surprises!

Mrs Noah has a surprise

Mrs Noah was very, very annoyed. She had just sold her goats at the market for two pieces of silver but on the way home a gang had robbed her in the olive grove.

'One day someone will give that Mavis Mugger and her gang what they deserve,' said Mrs Noah angrily to herself.

'Hello, dear,' called Mr Noah, as he locked up his fast food bar for the day. 'Did you have a good day at the market?'

'No! I sold the goats but that terrible gang robbed me and now I'm very, very annoyed.'

Mr Noah took her hand as they walked home. 'You're not hurt, are you, dear?'

Mrs Noah shook her head.

Mr Noah sighed. 'I don't know. The young people these days. It was never like this in my young days. When we get home, you put your feet up and I'll cook you a nice meal.'

That evening their son Shem stopped by to tell them that his wife was going to have a baby.

Mrs Noah was so pleased that she forgot that she was very, very annoyed.

'I'm going to be a granny,' Mrs Noah said to herself as she cleaned the old family cradle. It wasn't the best cradle in the world . . . Mr Noah was not really very good at making things, but it was good enough. The thought of having a baby to rock to sleep made Mrs Noah smile.

* * *

Over the next few months life in their town got steadily worse with the gangs robbing and bullying people. It wasn't safe to go out at night alone because rival gangs were roaming the streets.

Mrs Noah bought a big bolt for the door of their house but sometimes, at night, she and Mr Noah felt afraid.

Life was becoming very unhappy on earth. Mr Noah hardly felt safe just going to the woods to find berries for his milkshakes.

'What a world to bring a baby into,' said Mrs Noah as she rocked her newborn granddaughter to sleep one evening.

'Mavis Mugger was bullying people into handing over their food today. I don't know what the world is coming to, dear, I really don't,' said Mr Noah as he buttered his toast.

There was nothing Mr Noah liked better than a snack of toast and honey. He spread the honey very thickly when he thought Mrs Noah wasn't looking.

'Scrumptious,' said Mr Noah.

'Noah!' said a loud voice.

'It's the Lord God!' said Mrs Noah.

'Noah!' said the loud voice again.

'Mmmm,' said Mr Noah, with his mouth full of toast.

'Noah!'

'Yes, Lord?' said Mrs Noah.

'I'm fed up with all this nonsense,' said God. 'People are doing very wicked things and spoiling the lovely world I made. I'm getting pretty angry with them. Well, you and your family are all right. And the baby is rather well made, don't you think?

'Anyway, I'm getting rid of *everything* that is spoiling my world. But I want to keep you and your family to look after things. I want you to build an ark.'

'Ark?' said Mrs Noah.

'Yes. An ark. Noah, are you listening?'

'Mmmm,' said Mr Noah through a sticky beard. 'I'm sorry, you see, the honey . . .'

'Do you think you could possibly get a pen and write down the instructions?'

'Right,' said Mrs Noah.

So God explained the measurements and the design of the ark. Mr Noah listened carefully and tried to stop his knees knocking at the thought of what God wanted him to do. And Mrs Noah made some notes.

'Is that clear?' said God at last.

'Yes, Lord,' said Mrs Noah, 'but . . . er . . . you mean you want him to make this . . . out of wood?'

'Yes.'

'With a hammer and nails and things?'

'Yes. And it's all right to cut down the trees for the wood because I'm going to grow forests of new ones after the flood.'

'Flood?' said Mrs Noah.

'Flood?' repeated Mr Noah. 'Flood! You do know I can't swim, don't you?'

'Get the ark right and you won't need to swim.'

(Story continues on page 8)

ANIMAL ART

Animals can be quite easy to draw. Start with an oval shape, then add to it.

Try to copy these.

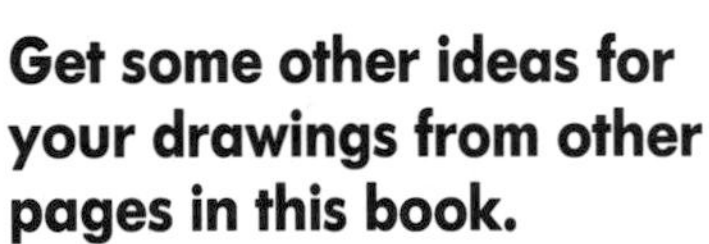

Get some other ideas for your drawings from other pages in this book.

PENGUIN PATTERNS

Carefully press out the penguin shape from the cover. Use this to help you draw some patterns like this.

Colour them carefully. Why not use one of your patterns to make a card of some kind?

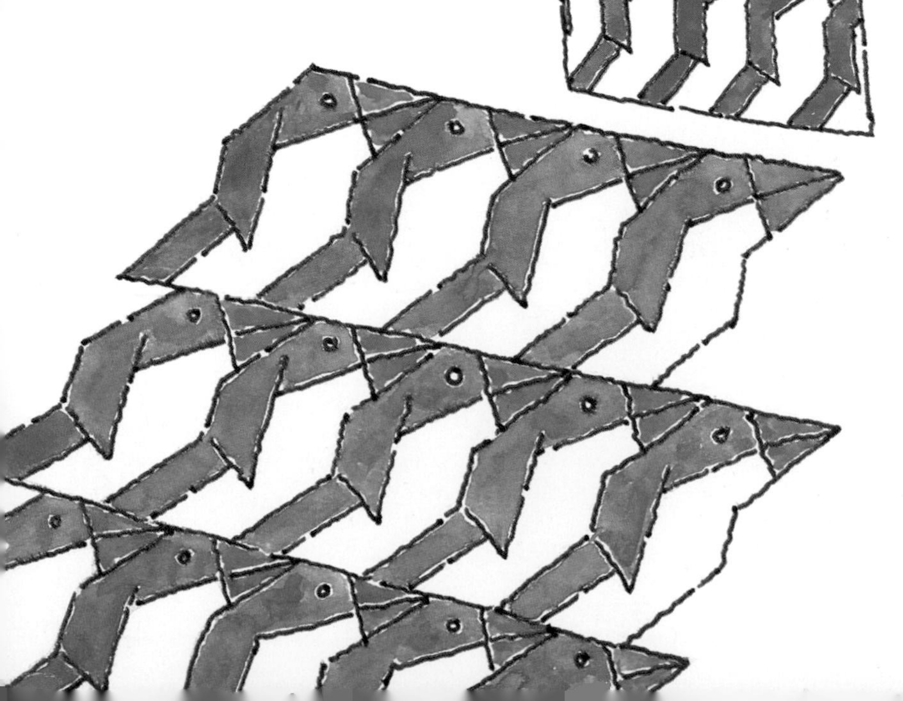

FOLDED PAPER ANIMALS

1 Fold a piece of paper in half.

2 Draw a simple animal shape. Here are two examples.

3 Colour and cut out.

You might like to use these with a model ark. Why not try making one from an empty cereal box?

DOUBLE ANIMAL PICTURES

YOU NEED:

2 animal pictures from a magazine, cut to the same size
a piece of thick paper about the same height as the pictures but twice as long
scissors
glue
a ruler

1 Fold the thick piece of paper into concertina folds about 1cm across.

2 Cut one of the pictures into strips the same width as these concertina folds.

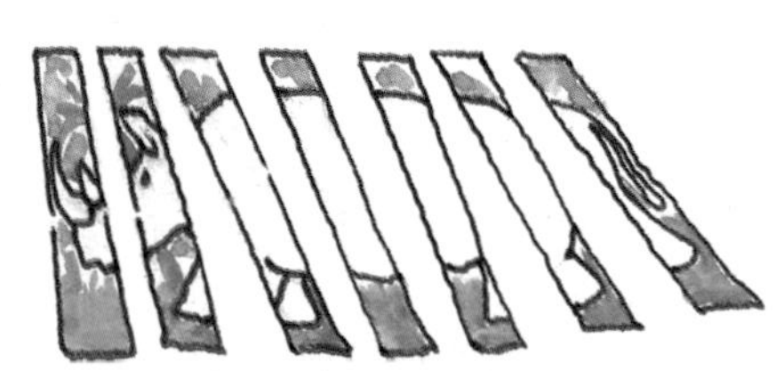

3 Stick these strips of picture onto every alternate fold.

4 Do the same with the second picture.

Now put your concertina folder where everyone can see it. If you look at it from the left you will see one picture, and if you look at it from the right you will see the other.

SOMETHING FISHY!

Can you finish off this fishy pattern? There are more dots on the inside front cover for you to photocopy. Use these to design other patterns.

Mrs Noah gets ready

The next morning Mr Noah made a start on the ark. He had wanted to open up his fast food bar as usual, but Mrs Noah reminded him what God had said.

'But I'm so bad at woodwork,' moaned Mr Noah. 'Maybe I could start this evening?'

'Look,' said Mrs Noah, 'when God tells you something I think he means you to do it. You make a start and I'll go and get the kids to help.'

So Shem, Ham and Japheth came to help their father build the ark.

'Are you sure we should be doing this?' said Shem as they cut down the trees.

'Seems a crazy plan to me,' said Ham as they sawed the wood.

'Just build it and stop questioning,' said Mrs Noah briskly.

Mavis Mugger and her gang laughed at Noah and his family. 'An ark? A boat? Here? What an idiot you are, Noah! What's it for?'

'God told me to build it because he's sending a flood.'

'Flood! Flood!' shrieked Mavis Mugger nearly falling over laughing. 'It hardly ever rains here.'

'Do we really have to do this, Dad?' said Japheth. 'I feel such a fool.'

'It will be Mavis Mugger who will look foolish when we are all safe on the ark.'

* * *

For days and days Mrs Noah helped to cut down trees and saw them into planks, paint the ark with pitch to make it waterproof, and make sandwiches.

All the family had blisters on their hands and they were fed up with Mavis Mugger and her gang making fun of them.

'Well,' said Mrs Noah. 'We've done what God told us to do and it looks pretty good.'

'Mmmm,' said Mr Noah, his mouth full of toast and honey.

'Noah,' said a loud voice.

'Mmmm . . .'

'Now for more instructions,' said God.

'Yoummmump!' said Noah.

'I know I made you jump,' said God. 'It was my little joke. I couldn't resist it when I saw you with that toast and honey.'

'Have we done it right?' asked Mrs Noah nervously.

'It's a wonderful job. I do appreciate it when people listen and do as I ask them. Now, here are the rest of the instructions...'

So God told them about getting plenty of food together, gathering in lots of animals, and about the rain he was going to send.

'Got all that?' asked God.

'Yes, Lord,' said Mrs Noah, 'but er...I'm just a little bit worried about these animals. I mean, lions and things...er...well, how do I stop them eating the sheep and goats?'

'That's why I told you to make all those different rooms,' said God. 'You'll also have to make rules, Mrs Noah.'

'Yes... OK,' said Mrs Noah uncertainly.

'You'll manage,' said God. 'Be firm, Mrs Noah. I know you can be. And I will always be there looking after you.'

Mr and Mrs Noah smiled and held hands. 'Thanks,' they said.

'The weather forecast is rain, rain and more rain,' said God. 'So get the shopping done quickly.'

The next day Mrs Noah took her family to the shops. They had an enormous shopping list! They needed enough food to feed all the animals and themselves for months, as well as all sorts of things for 'just in case'. Shem suggested a rope to tie up any difficult animals, Ham suggested a butterfly net, and Mr Noah said, 'and we need lots of honey.'

* * *

Then the rain started and Mrs Noah organized everyone to load up the ark with the food and clothes and everything else that they would need. It wasn't going to be easy to live for weeks in a floating zoo.

'Now, let me think,' Mrs Noah said to herself as she loaded on sacks of wheat, lentils and vegetables. 'We'll have to have hot soup or we'll catch cold in all this rain. And I'm still not clear how I'm going to stop all these animals from eating each other. Oh dearie me, what a to-do.'

(Story continues on page 14)

MRS NOAH'S SNACKS

△ ASK A GROWN-UP TO HELP

Always wash your hands before cooking, and remember to clear up afterwards.

LION SALAD

YOU NEED:

for each person:
a big plate
a carrot
celery
a tomato
a cheese triangle
some grated cheese

Carefully cut the carrot and celery into sticks. Halve the tomato. Now arrange the vegetables on the plates to make a lion's face.

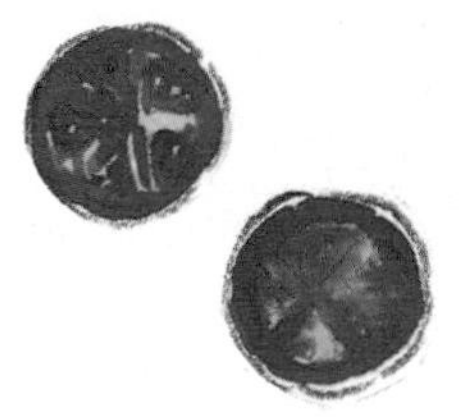

ELEPHANT SALAD

YOU NEED:

a tomato halved and topped with grated cheese
celery sticks
carrot sticks

This is made like Lion Salad but you need to make it on a long dish or on a big chopping board.

FUN FRUIT SLICES

YOU NEED:

some fruit, e.g. oranges, apples, bananas or grapes
something to sprinkle on the fruit, e.g. sunflower seeds or raisins
a bowl or a plate

1 Slice the fruit, taking out any pips.

2 Arrange the slices in a pattern on the plate.

3 Sprinkle with seeds or raisins.

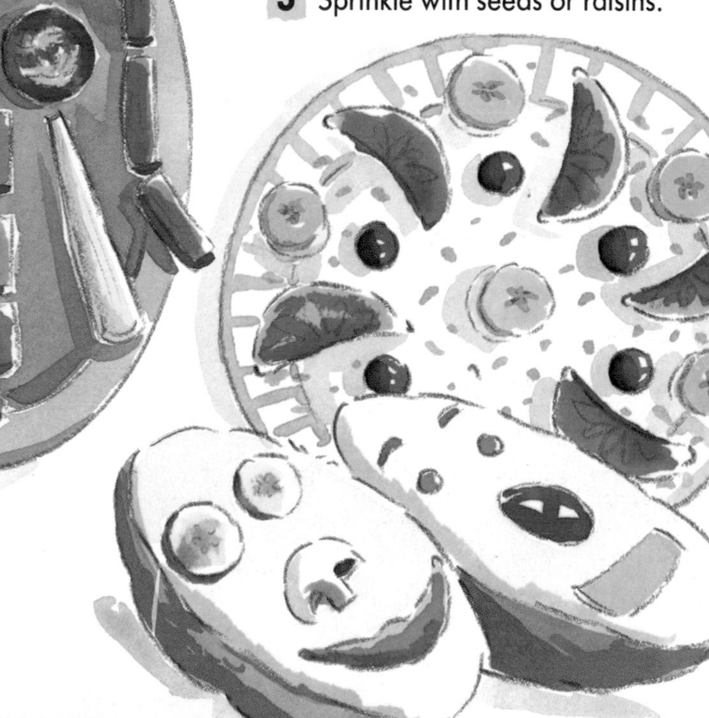

SMILEY POTATOES

YOU NEED:

for each person:
half a baked potato
cheese
some cooked vegetables, e.g. a few peas or beans, or salad vegetables, like sliced cucumber, a small tomato or mushroom

1 Cut the baked potato in half.

2 Make eyes out of peas or cucumber.

3 Make a nose out of tomato or a mushroom.

4 Make a big smile with a long green bean, or with a strip of cheese.

WHATEVER THE WEATHER...

BE A WEATHER FORECASTER

Modern weather forecasting is based on information from high-tech weather stations around the world and from space satellites. People have always tried to predict the weather and, before this technology was available, they used to look carefully at the world of nature to forecast the weather.

Here are some ways to be a weather forecaster. Try them out!

Bring some seaweed home from the beach. Or find a fir cone in the woods. Keep the seaweed or cone outside in a sheltered place. If the seaweed goes limp and rubbery, rain is on the way. If it is hard and dry, it will probably be dry. If the fir cone opens up its scales, it will be dry. If they close up, it will rain.

WEATHER LORE

There are many folklore weather sayings. Test them to see if they are true.

If you hear a cock crowing
before the sun has come up,
it will rain.

Swallows flying high means no rain in the sky,
Swallows near the ground means rain will come around.

Red sky at night, shepherd's delight,
Red sky in the morning, shepherd's warning.

If you see cattle lying down, it will rain. People think that the cattle want to keep a patch dry!

When clouds appear like rocks and towers,
The earth's refreshed by frequent showers.

Frogs know when it will rain. They turn a brighter green in wet weather and are yellowish brown in dry weather.

When sea birds fly out towards the sea in the morning it means it will be fair weather. If you see them flying inland, it means a storm is on the way.

WEATHER FLAWS

Some things people say about the weather are wrong!

'Lightning never strikes twice in the same place.'
Wrong. Tall buildings such as the skyscrapers in big cities, and churches, are often struck by lightning. There is a special metal lightning conductor on the top of tall buildings that takes the electricity safely to the ground. Look out for these.

'Thunder turns milk sour.'
Wrong. It is the hot and humid weather that often comes with thunder that actually turns the milk sour.

What's worse than raining cats and dogs?
Hailing taxis.

Why do people carry umbrellas in the rain?
Because umbrellas can't walk.

Where do cowboys keep their drinking water?
In their ten-gallon hats.

WEATHER FACTS

Death Valley in California, USA, is one of the world's hottest places... sometimes it is about 56°C. We would find it much too hot to be out in the sun for long at only 36°C.

In northern Europe it used to be much colder than it is now. It was so cold that the River Thames froze completely and the ice was so thick that 'frost fairs' were held on the ice. People roasted pigs over fires built on the ice!

One of the many weather satellites that orbit the earth to forecast the weather is called NOAA (Noah).

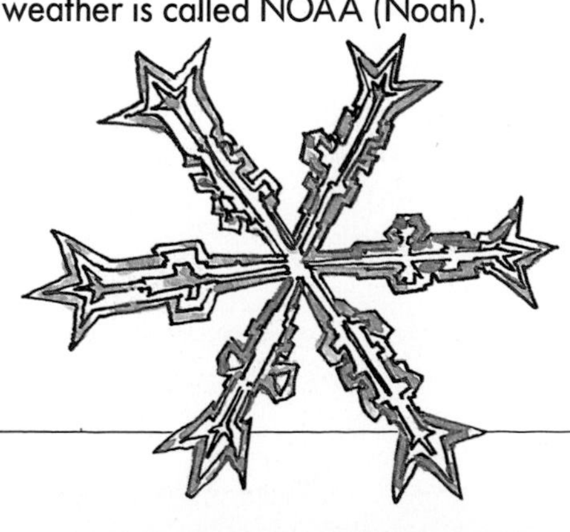

The biggest raindrops fall during summer thunderstorms. Some can be almost a centimetre across.

The biggest snowflake ever measured was 5cm across.

The biggest hailstones ever recorded fell in Ohio, USA in 1981. Some weighed as much as 3.6kg each!

A tornado is a small but very violent funnel of wind that twists around at about 300kmph. These tornadoes can pick up anything in their path including houses and cars!

Mrs Noah keeps her feet dry

The rain went on, day after day, and it began to get very muddy in the town. Mrs Noah made a long list of all the animals that she was going to get into the ark. Unfortunately she dropped her list in the mud once or twice, but she could just about read it and called the family together to give them their instructions...

'Off you go, now,' said Mrs Noah at last. 'Find a male and a female . . . two of every kind of animal.'

'You're sure we don't need to bring in the fishes and whales, dearest?' said Mr Noah.

'No, they will be fine. Now, do put on your wellies, dearest, or you'll get wet feet.'

The Noah family went all over the countryside finding two of every kind of creature. There were hundreds and hundreds of them! And as they went up the gangplank into the ark the noise was deafening!

'Well,' squawked Mrs Hornbill, 'at least we're out of all that rain.'

'I hope they are going to put up a few more perches,' said Mr Robin. 'It's a bit crowded in here.'

'Nothing to worry about,' said Mr Woodpecker. 'We'll soon drill a few more holes for all of us.'

'I wouldn't do that,' said Mrs Parrot. 'I think that we're going on a cruise and your holes might let in the water.'

'Well I want a very large hole,' said Mr Great Grey Owl. 'And did you know that you parrots are making more noise than the rest of us put together?'

'Not as much as the monkeys!' laughed Mrs Kookaburra.

'Oh, do be quiet, all of you,' said Mrs Hummingbird as she flitted from perch to perch. 'There are no flowers here. I need the nectar from flowers to feed on. We might die of starvation.'

'Oh no you won't,' said Japheth arriving with a whole tray of assorted bird food. 'Here are jars of honey water for the hummingbirds, seeds of all sorts and sizes, best quality wild bird food, and a bird food cake made with my own hands. No more complaining.'

'How I'm going to get this baby to sleep in this racket, I don't know,' said Mrs Noah.

'I'll help,' said Mrs Nightingale. 'I'll sit here and sing.'

'How kind,' said Mrs Noah with a smile.

* * *

The rain went on and on, day after day.

Mavis Mugger and her friends were still laughing at the Noah family, but they were beginning to look a bit worried.

The rain went on and on and on.

The ark was almost afloat. Mr Noah pulled up the gang plank and suddenly, with a great lurch, the ark floated off. Mavis Mugger was left behind. She was very wet and muddy, and she wasn't laughing now.

(Story continues on page 20)

FEEDING THE BIRDS

MAKE A BIRD CAKE

This is easy to make and a good way to help birds find food in winter.

YOU NEED:

a bowl of very hot water
a smaller bowl
a wooden spoon
1 cup of suet
1 cup of any of the following:
- **food scraps (e.g. bread, cheese, fruit or *unsalted* nuts) or dry food (e.g. dried fruit or plain breakfast cereal) or bird seed from the pet shop**

old yoghurt pots, each with a long, knotted piece of string threaded through a hole in the bottom
a plate

1 Put the suet in the smaller bowl and put this in the hot water. This will melt the suet.

2 Add the other ingredients. For every cup of food, you need one cup of suet.

3 Stir it all together.

4 Tip the mixture into the yoghurt pots and put a bit on the plate. Let it set.

5 Using the string, hang up the pots in a safe place where cats can't reach them. The cake on the plate can go in lumps on a bird table or window sill.

⚠ WARNING

Don't use anything very salty. Don't give bird cake or peanuts to birds in the spring. There is plenty of food around then and their babies might choke on nuts.

WATER IS IMPORTANT

Birds need water to drink and to bathe in. You can put out a dish of water all year round. Change the water every day and in the winter put a ball in the water (this helps to keep the water from freezing). In very cold weather you might need to crack the ice.

MAKE A BIRD FEEDER

YOU NEED:

a plastic bottle
something to make holes in the bottle
string
3 pieces of thin wood
scissors
peanuts (unsalted)

1 Make 2 holes on opposite sides of the bottle for string to hang it up.

2 Make 6 holes for the pieces of wood.

3 Push the wood through to make sticks for the birds to sit on.

4 Make a row of slits down the bottle. Take care not to cut the slits too close to the perches or the bottle will split.

5 Fill the bottle with the peanuts. Screw the top on and hang it up well away from cats.

THE RAINBOW GAME
1
2
3
4
5
6
7
14
15
16
17
18
19
20
21
22
23
24
25
26
34
35
36
37
38
39
40
41
42
43
44
45
46
47
51
52
53
54
55
56
57
58
59
60
61
62
63
64
65

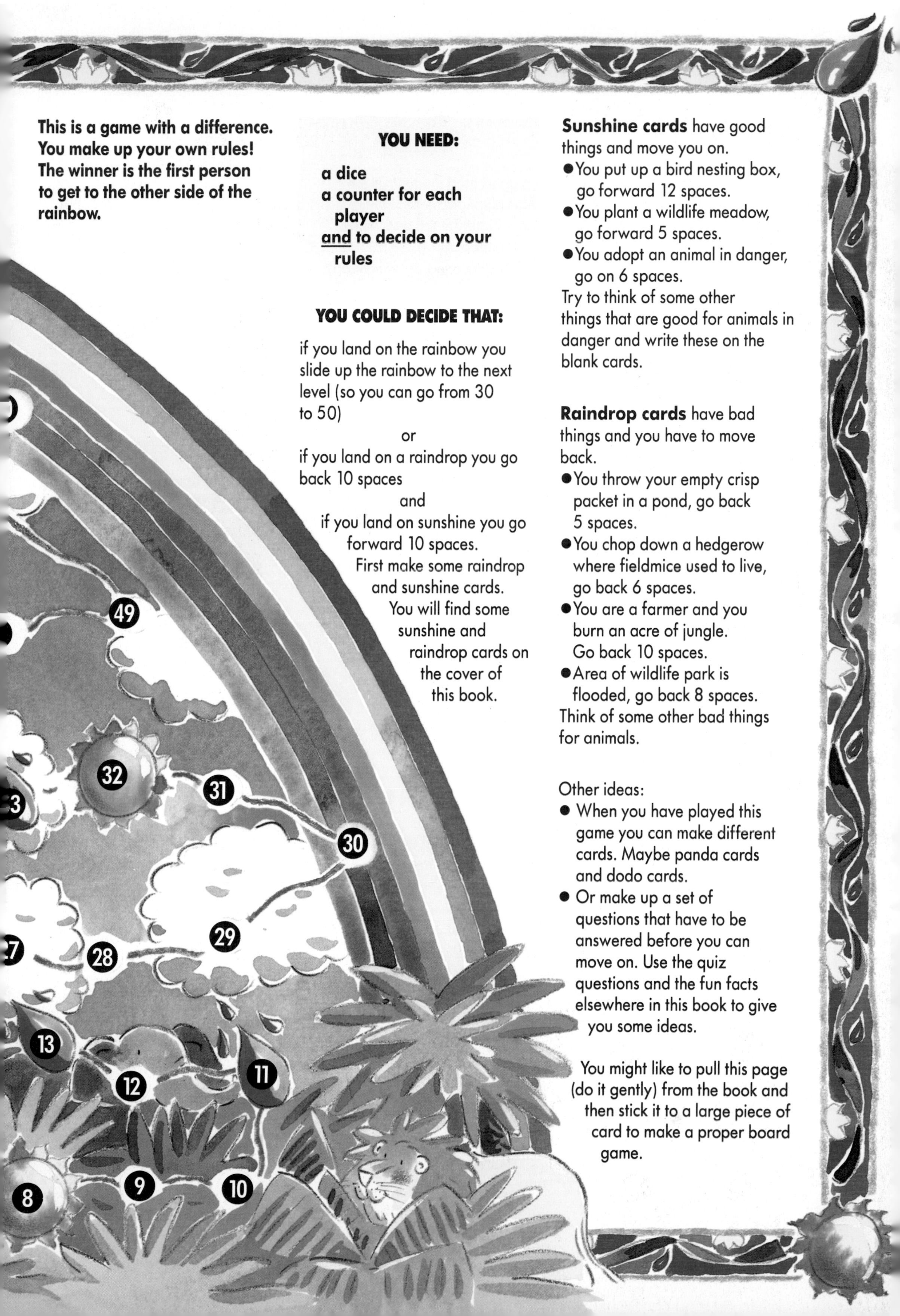

This is a game with a difference. You make up your own rules! The winner is the first person to get to the other side of the rainbow.

YOU NEED:

a dice
a counter for each player
and to decide on your rules

YOU COULD DECIDE THAT:

if you land on the rainbow you slide up the rainbow to the next level (so you can go from 30 to 50)

or

if you land on a raindrop you go back 10 spaces

and

if you land on sunshine you go forward 10 spaces.

First make some raindrop and sunshine cards. You will find some sunshine and raindrop cards on the cover of this book.

Sunshine cards have good things and move you on.

- You put up a bird nesting box, go forward 12 spaces.
- You plant a wildlife meadow, go forward 5 spaces.
- You adopt an animal in danger, go on 6 spaces.

Try to think of some other things that are good for animals in danger and write these on the blank cards.

Raindrop cards have bad things and you have to move back.

- You throw your empty crisp packet in a pond, go back 5 spaces.
- You chop down a hedgerow where fieldmice used to live, go back 6 spaces.
- You are a farmer and you burn an acre of jungle. Go back 10 spaces.
- Area of wildlife park is flooded, go back 8 spaces.

Think of some other bad things for animals.

Other ideas:

- When you have played this game you can make different cards. Maybe panda cards and dodo cards.
- Or make up a set of questions that have to be answered before you can move on. Use the quiz questions and the fun facts elsewhere in this book to give you some ideas.

You might like to pull this page (do it gently) from the book and then stick it to a large piece of card to make a proper board game.

ANIMAL FUN

DO YOU KNOW?

1 Which bird flies the greatest distance?

2 Which animals have the biggest teeth?

3 How do water animals like ducks and beavers keep waterproof?

4 Which animals can jump the farthest?

5 Which animal can run the fastest over short distances?

6 Do any mammals lay eggs?

7 Complete this saying: 'As dead as a . . . '

8 These tiny animals live in the sea and build enormous, beautifully coloured structures called reefs.

9 These tiny birds hover beside plants and drink the nectar from flowers.

10 Do tigers live in Africa?

11 How do animals such as gerbils keep cool in the desert?

12 Where do yaks live?

(Answers on page 32)

FUN FACTS

The biggest land mammal is the African elephant. A bull (male) is usually about 3m tall and weighs over 5 tonnes.

The biggest one ever was nearly 4m tall and weighed over 12 tonnes!

The biggest meat-eating land animal that ever lived was the dinosaur *Tyrannosaurus rex*.

The tallest mammal is the giraffe. Adult males are usually 5.5m tall and the tallest one ever known was almost 6m tall.

CONSERVATION QUIZ

1 What is the rare Chinese bear that zoo keepers have been trying to breed in captivity for many years?

2 About how many tigers are left in the world: 20, 2,000 or 20,000?

3 Which three of the animals listed here have been successfully bred in zoos and returned to the wild?

Przewalski's horse

Hawaiian goose

Lion

Arabian oryx

Emperor penguin

The smallest non-flying mammal is the Savi's pygmy shrew. It weighs less than a sugar lump and is just over 6cm long.

The smallest flying mammal is the tiny bumblebee bat from Thailand. It was only discovered in 1973 (presumably because it is so small no one noticed it) and is just 3.3cm long.

The fastest flying bird (in level flight) is the swift.

Most cats don't like water, but when tigers get too hot they stand in water to cool down.

Bats have large ears and have the best hearing of any land mammals.

A Canadian porcupine has over 30,000 sharp quills, each about 12cm long. Not surprisingly, when it is attacked and it stabs its enemy, the enemy tends to run away!

Lemurs are little animals that live in the jungles of Madagascar. Farmers want the land to grow crops so they burn the jungle. This means that the lemur has less and less space to live in.

The beautiful bird of paradise is an endangered species because once it used to be shot for its feathers and now its jungle home is being destroyed.

Tamarins are tiny monkeys that live in South America. There are many different kinds. There are so few golden lion tamarins now that they would die out if they weren't bred in zoos and protected in a special reserve in Rio de Janeiro.

4 What animal, now protected by law, used to roam on the plains of North America? (So many were shot by early settlers that they nearly died out.)

5 Which North American eagle was endangered when farmers sprayed their crops with poisons to kill insect pests? (The poison got into the rivers and into the fish that this eagle eats.)

6 About how many whooping cranes are left in the world: 10, 100, 1,000 or 10,000?

7 Why do hunters shoot elephants?

8 What bird became extinct in 1914 after extensive hunting by North American settlers?

9 What enormous mammals are shot with harpoons for their meat and blubber?

10 What amphibious animals are hunted so that shoes and handbags can be made from their skins?

CONSERVATION FACTS

Many zoos and wildlife parks around the world breed animals that are in danger of becoming extinct. This 'captive breeding' means that when the babies born in the zoos have grown up, they can eventually be returned to the wild.

Wildlife parks and national parks are specially protected areas of land where animals can live safely in the wild.

Many animals would become extinct if it were not for the work of zoos and protected parks.

Mrs Noah stays afloat

Life was very busy on the ark, what with the feeding, the cleaning out and stopping all the arguments. Mrs Noah remembered what God had said about making rules. She had made a start with her list, and everyone else wanted to help.

'We say that spiders should not be allowed to make their webs anywhere near where we are flying,' said the flies.

'And we think that the squirrels should have more nuts,' said the squirrels.

'No one else should be allowed to eat the bamboo shoots,' said Mr Panda. 'It's all we really like to eat and they might run out.'

'Now, now,' said Mrs Noah. 'One at a time and we'll make up the rules. Then everybody, I mean *everybody* . . . ' she looked hard at the monkeys who were always up to tricks, 'everybody obeys the rules.'

The rain went on and on for days. There was no sign of land anywhere. Even the tall mountains had disappeared.

Mrs Noah was worried because there was nowhere to hang the washing to dry. Mr Noah was worried because he was running out of honey. Japheth was worried because tempers were getting frayed. And Shem was worried because the lions were getting fed up with being good. They said that if the buffalo made funny faces at them once more, buffalo-burgers would be on the menu.

Ham was just worried about everything.

'Don't worry, son,' Mrs Noah said as she strung the washing across a line that the spiders had spun for her. 'It will all work out all right. God knows what he is doing.'

One day, it stopped raining! Just for a while.

'Oh, look,' said Mrs Noah. 'Enough blue sky to make a sailor a pair of shorts.'

Everyone began to feel more cheerful.

The next day, it stopped raining for a whole morning.

'About time too,' said Mrs Noah happily. 'Today there is enough blue sky to make a sailor a pair of trousers. Let's have a party!'

All the animals cheered and Mr and Mrs Noah went off to prepare a party.

(Story continues on page 22)

MRS NOAH'S PARTY FOOD

CHEESY PORCUPINES

△ **Take care with cocktail sticks.**

YOU NEED:

an orange
cocktail sticks
cubes of cheese
a knife

1 Wash the orange and cut it in half. Ask before you use a sharp knife.

2 Cut the cheese into cubes and put these on the cocktail sticks.

3 Arrange the cocktail sticks on the halves of orange.

4 You can add raisins for eyes and nose.

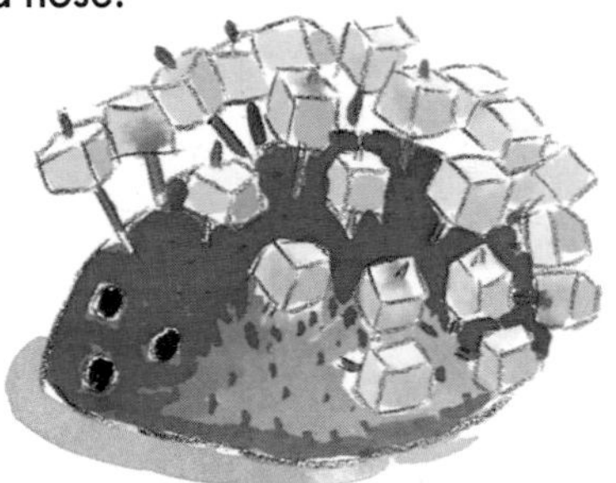

MRS NOAH'S NIBBLES

YOU NEED:

stoned dates
currants or raisins or something else yummy to stuff the dates with. Marzipan is good, so is soft cheese.

1 Put your chosen filling into the hole left by the date stone.

2 If your filling is pale in colour you could use a raisin to make an eye. Then you can call them 'Mrs Noah's fish'.

MRS NOAH'S NOG

YOU NEED:

2 lemons or some lemon juice
honey
hot water
2 mugs

1 Squeeze the juice out of the lemons and put it in the mugs.

2 Put a large teaspoonful of honey in each mug.

3 Add the water and stir.

This is very good hot for getting rid of rainy day sniffles and sneezes. If you let it cool down you can float slices of lemon and ice cubes in it for a delicious party drink.

RABBITS IN THE GRASS

YOU NEED:

a tin of pear halves
a green jelly
marshmallows
almonds

1 Make up the jelly.

2 When the jelly has set, chop it up and put it on a plate.

3 Put the pear halves on the grass to look like rabbits.

4 Give them almond ears and marshmallow tails.

RAINBOW JELLIES

YOU NEED:

patience . . . this takes quite a long time!
several different colour jellies
several individual glass dishes
a bowl
ice cubes

△ **ASK A GROWN-UP TO HELP**

1 Make up one jelly in the bowl, using only half the quantity of water. Then add ice cubes to cool it down. Stir these around and the jelly will cool down quite quickly.

2 When it is almost set, pour a little jelly into each glass dish.

3 When this is set, make up the next jelly. Again, use ice cubes.

4 When it is cold, carefully pour a little on top of the other jelly in the dishes.

5 Keep adding jelly like this in layers.

If you are *very* patient and have lots of different-coloured jellies, you might be able to make most of the colours of the rainbow. Can you remember them? (Look at page 25.)

Mrs Noah nears dry land

One day, it didn't rain at all. The animals came out on deck and gave a great loud cheer. It didn't rain the next day, or the next.

'Maybe there is some dry land somewhere,' said Mr Noah. 'Mr and Mrs Eagle, could you possibly fly really high and see what you can see?'

'Us?' said Mr Eagle. 'Do you realize who you are talking to? The king of birds...'

'And queen of birds,' put in Mrs Eagle.

'We have been shut in this stinking boat for days and you expect us, the king — and queen — of birds, to . . . '

'I'll go,' said Mr Raven, giving the eagles a hard stare. 'Some creatures are so stuck up and proud . . . '

'Will you really?' said Mr Noah. 'That is so kind of you. Now, don't get lost.'

'Take care,' said Mrs Raven. 'I'll wait here on top of the ark until you come back.'

So Mr Raven flew off into the unknown.

He flew until he thought his wings might fall off, but there was no land anywhere. He made it back to the ark, exhausted, and everyone (except the eagles) treated him like a hero.

'That was very brave of you, Raven,' said Mr Dove. 'Next time, I will go. I want to prove that we doves are brave and strong.'

'Now, now,' said Mr Noah, 'no one has to prove anything, but you may go next.'

So the next week Mr Dove flew off. He flew for hours and hours, but there was no land to be seen. He too, just made it back to the ark.

'My turn next,' said Mrs Dove. So the next week, Mrs Dove set off from the ark. She was getting very tired and was thinking of turning back when she saw an olive branch sticking out of the water. She got very excited. She landed on the branch and plucked at one of the twigs to show Mr and Mrs Noah.

'Land,' she said breathlessly as she got back to the ark. 'Well, almost land — the top of a tree is showing over there.'

That night there was a great celebration. Everyone was very excited.

'Land has been sighted,' sang Mrs Nightingale to the baby.

'Oh, dry land at last,' said Mrs Noah as she gathered in her washing.

'You bees will have to get busy, you know,' said Mr Noah. 'I'm about to eat the last of the honey. I'm relying on you.'

'Dear Noah,' said Mrs Bee (who was really a queen but preferred to be plain Mrs Bee), 'you have been so wonderful to all of us that we will make honey for you always.' She sat on his nose and beamed at him.

'Well . . . er . . . how kind,' said Mr Noah.

'We're going to go and find out if there's land out there now, Mrs Noah,' said the doves. 'If we don't come back, you'll know that we have found somewhere to build our nest.'

'It's getting a little bit urgent, I think,' whispered Mrs Dove to Mrs Noah. 'Eggs on the way, you see.'

'Oh, well, off you go then.' The doves flew off.

Everyone waited and waited. They all had a cup of tea and a little munch of something to fill the time*.

*(You can find Mrs Noah's Snacks on page 11.
Story continues on page 28)

SCIENCE FUN

MAKE A RAINBOW

YOU NEED:

a bowl of water
a flat mirror
a torch (on a sunny day you can do this with a shaft of sunlight)

Rest the mirror against the edge of the bowl and shine the torch at it through the water. Catch the light on the ceiling or on a piece of white paper.

If you don't have a mirror, it is possible to do this with a jar of water on a window-sill on a sunny day.

BENDING LIGHT

YOU NEED:

a glass of water
a drinking straw

Put the straw into the water and look closely. The straw looks bent! This is because the light rays have bent as they pass from the air into the water and back into the air again.

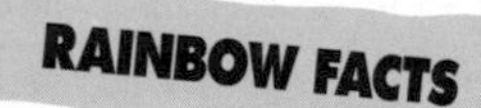

RAINBOW FACTS

Rainbows are formed when the sun shines while rain is still falling.

To see a rainbow at its best you need to turn your back on the sun and look towards the falling raindrops.

The rainbow is formed when the sunlight is bent inside the raindrop and the light is split up into the seven colours of the spectrum.

If there are two or more bends of light in the raindrops this causes a secondary rainbow. This is much more difficult to see and it appears with the colours reversed.

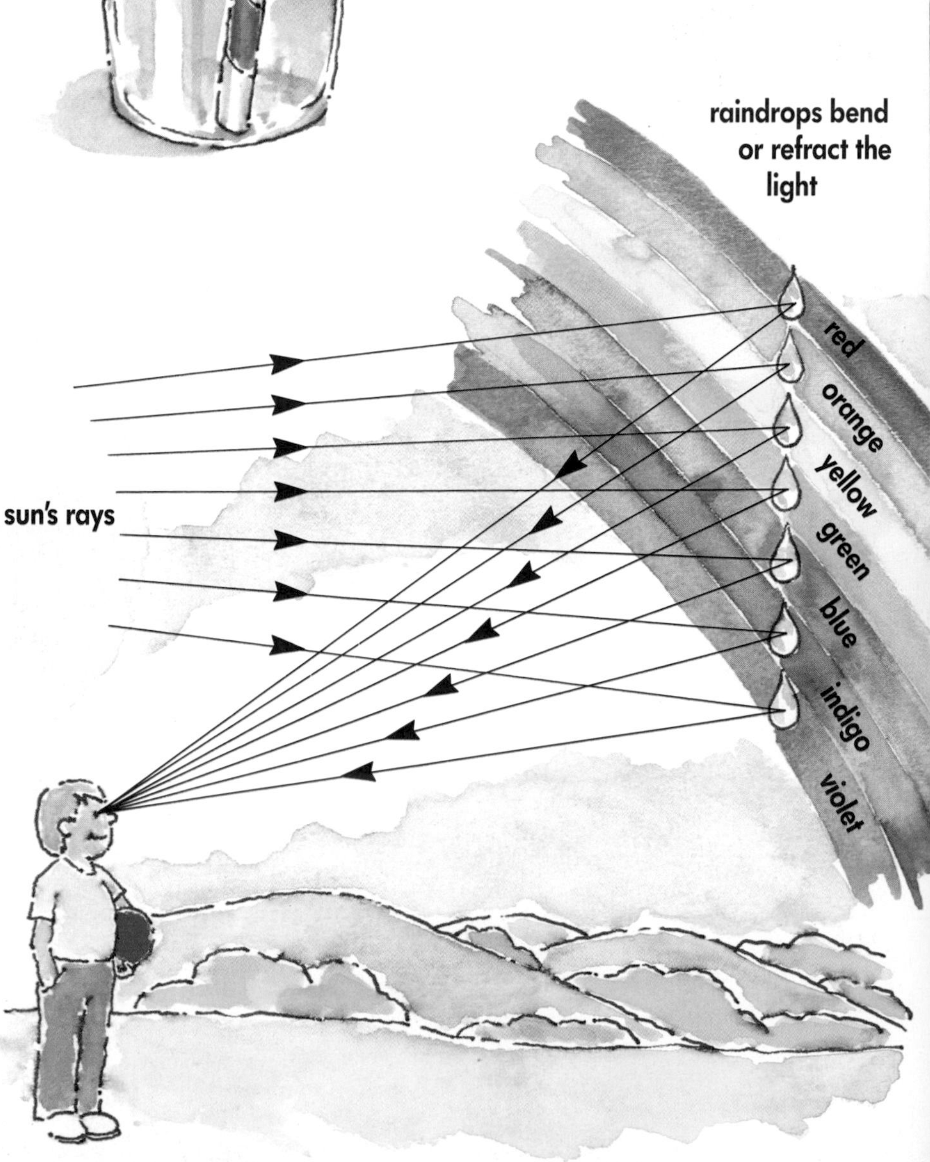

MAKE A RAINBOW SPINNER

If you press out the coloured circle on the back cover and put a pencil or a cocktail stick exactly through the middle of it, you will have a spinning top. Spin the top and see what happens.

As you spin the disc the colours merge together to make a dirty white colour. If the colours were completely pure (as they are in a rainbow) it would appear to go really white.

MAKE RAIN

△ ASK A GROWN-UP TO HELP

YOU NEED:

a kettle of water
some ice cubes
a saucepan

1 Put the ice cubes into the saucepan for a few minutes and stir them around.

2 Ask an adult to boil the kettle and to hold the cold saucepan in the steam. You will see rain falling from the cold surface of the pan.

Why does this happen? When water boils, the liquid becomes a gas — water vapour — which we often call steam.

When it meets the cold surface of the pan it turns back into a liquid — water.

PAINT A RAINBOW

YOU NEED:

paper
a paintbrush
water
paint in these colours:
red, yellow, blue, and black

1 Paint a wide red arc on the outside.

2 Wash your brush and paint a yellow arc inside the red one, leaving a gap.

3 In the gap, paint with mixed yellow and red — orange.

4 Leave another gap and paint a blue arc.

5 In the gap, paint with blue and yellow mixed — green.

6 Next to the blue you need indigo. This is blue with a little black and a little red in it.

7 On the inside paint violet — red with a little bit of blue in it.

If you put your picture out in gentle rain for a few seconds, it will look very watery — like a real rainbow. Let it dry, then put it up in your bedroom.

How many colours can you make? Try mixing some more colours.

How many blues can you make? Try painting a picture just with blues.

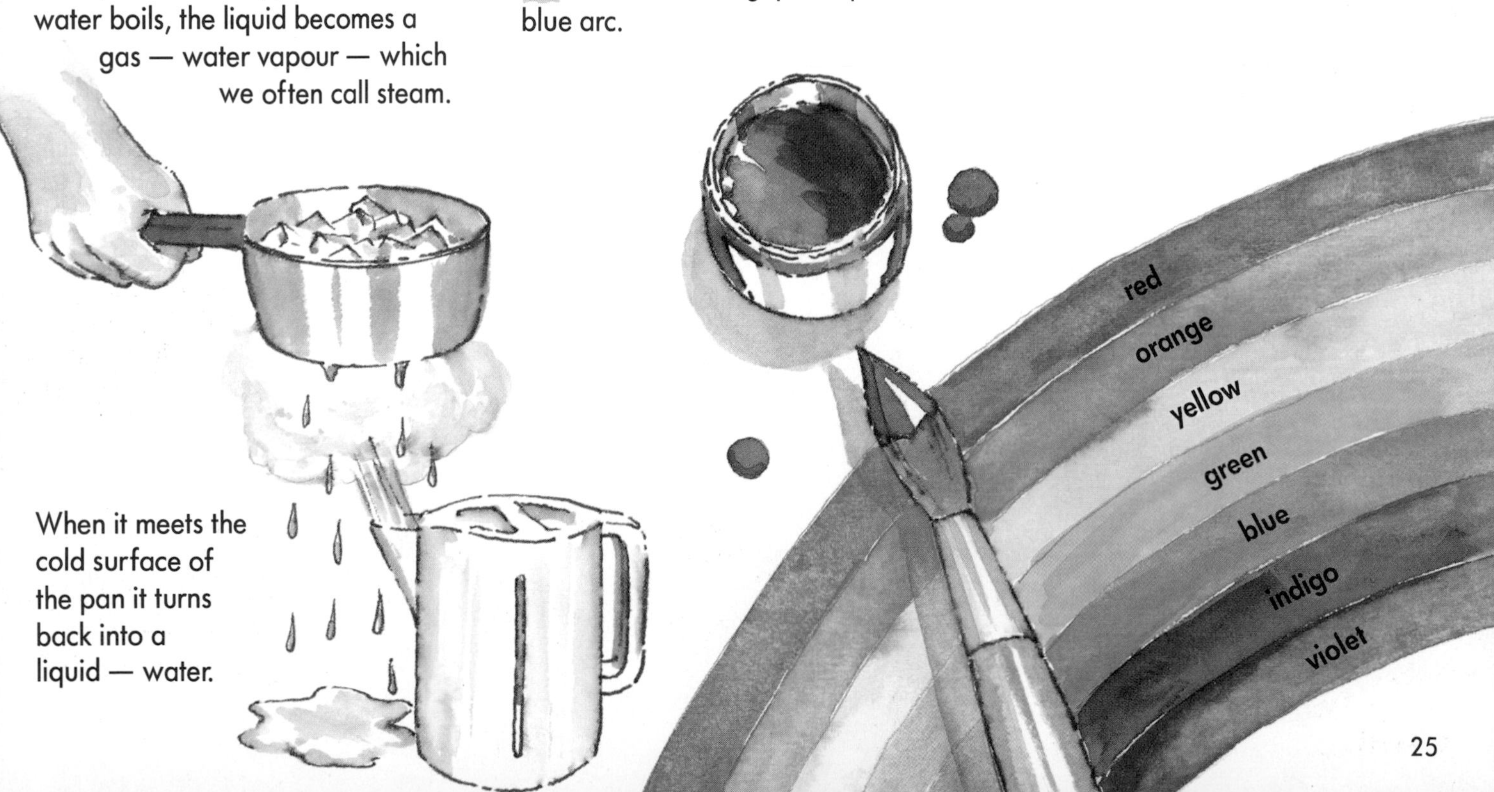

DESIGN A NEW WORLD

Imagine you are Mrs Noah. Draw a picture of what you would like your world to look like.

WHICH ANIMAL?

MAKING TRACKS

When the animals left the ark there was a lot of mud! Match each animal to its tracks in the mud. Answers on page 32.

Which animal is grey, has four legs and a trunk?
A mouse going on holiday.

Why do giraffes have long necks?
To join their heads to their bodies.

Which animal can jump higher than the Empire State Building?
They all can. Buildings can't jump.

What food did Mrs Noah buy for the porcupines?
Prickled onions.

ANIMAL ALPHABET

Ask a friend to help you to fill in an animal alphabet.

You could challenge someone else to make a completely different one. You might have to let them repeat your X, Y and Z!

A ____________
B ____________
C ____________
D ____________
E ____________
F ____________
G ____________
H ____________
I ____________
J ____________
K ____________
L ____________

M ____________
N ____________
O ____________
P ____________
Q ____________

R ____________
S ____________
T ____________
U ____________
V ____________
W ____________
X xerus (a squirrel)
Y ____________
Z ____________

Mrs Noah sees a rainbow

After Mr and Mrs Dove had left, the birds grew impatient.

'We're going to go too,' said Mr and Mrs Swan. 'If we get tired of flying we'll swim. Goodbye, everyone, goodbye.'

The animals waved goodbye.

'OK, this is it,' said Mr and Mrs Puffin. They flew up onto the top of the ark and made their little bobbing bows of thanks to Mr and Mrs Noah. 'Thank you. Thank you very much.'

'It was our pleasure,' said Mrs Noah, overcome with emotion. She got out her hanky and started to cry.

'Now, now, dear,' said Mr Noah, as the puffins flew off with their funny little wings flapping like fury.

Gradually all the birds began to leave. It was very hard to say goodbye. Even Mr and Mrs Eagle seemed grateful. Soon they were soaring up into the air until they were just specks in the blue sky.

One day, land was sighted. There was great excitement.

Mr Buffalo came to Mrs Noah that night, looking very anxious.

'A word in your ear, dear lady,' said Mr Buffalo quietly. 'Er . . . my wife and I . . . we . . . wondered if it would be possible for you to let us grass eaters go *before* you let out all those unspeakably dreadful big cats? You see, we seem, um . . . to be a bit unpopular with them . . . '

'You've been making silly faces at them again,' said Mrs Noah severely.

'Yes,' said Mr Buffalo, blushing with embarrassment. 'I'm most dreadfully sorry, but you see, if you let them go at the same time as us, we'll no sooner be down that gangplank then, . . . well . . . there's been talk of buffalo-burgers . . . '

'Don't worry,' said Mrs Noah. 'I'll fix it. Now go back to sleep.'

'Thank you,' said Mr Buffalo, putting a big sloppy kiss on Mrs Noah's cheek.

* * *

So when the ark finally came to rest on a big mountain, and when Mr Noah could see plenty of land, he let down the gangplank and Mr and Mrs Buffalo and some of the other animals left.

Shem wouldn't let the meat eaters go. The lions and tigers and cheetahs and all their cousins and relations were feeling very put out.

'That buffalo won't get far,' muttered Mr Lion under his breath.

'That he won't,' said Mr Jaguar.

'Hear, hear,' said the panthers and the leopards.

When all the grazing animals had disappeared into the forest, Shem let the meat eaters go.

'Please don't think badly of us,' said Mrs Lion. 'We really are very grateful for all that you have done.'

'Yes, thanks,' said the tigers.

'Thanks,' said the wolves.

'Bye,' said the brown bears.

Then Japheth looked into every corner of the ark to wake up sleeping spiders and he carried off the slow movers like the snails. At last all the animals had left the ark.

Mr and Mrs Noah smiled. They felt quite sad about leaving the ark. 'Thank you, Lord, for keeping us all safe,' they said.

'My pleasure,' said God. 'Thank you for doing as I asked. You did a very good job, but I'll never ask anyone to do what you did again. Now I'm going to make something new called a rainbow. Look . . . pretty good, eh?'

'Oh, lovely,' said Mrs Noah, clapping her hands in excitement.

'This rainbow is a special sign. It's a reminder of my promise never again to destroy the earth with a flood.'

'Good thing,' said Mr Noah into his beard. 'I don't think I could stand it again.'

'No, I don't suppose you could,' said God, laughing so much that it sounded like thunder. 'I don't suppose you could.'

Can you help me sort the animals? Those that eat plants need to leave the ark before the meat eaters.

MEAT EATERS		PLANT EATERS
☐	buffalo	☐
☐	cheetah	☐
☐	elk	☐
☐	zebra	☐
☐	antelope	☐
☐	hyena	☐
☐	lion	☐
☐	tiger	☐
☐	elephant	☐
☐	jaguar	☐
☐	leopard	☐
☐	gazelle	☐
☐	sheep	☐
☐	cougar	☐
☐	panther	☐
☐	horse	☐
☐	cattle	☐
☐	red deer	☐
☐	springbok	☐
☐	ox	☐
☐	giraffe	☐
☐	wolf	☐
☐	polar bear	☐

(Answers on page 32)

MRS NOAH'S WILDLIFE TIPS

1 PLANT A WILDLIFE GARDEN

If you grow plants, you will be helping to provide a place where wildlife can live. You don't need a big space. You could just have one corner of the yard as a wildlife garden.

Butterflies, beetles, bees and many other insects need plants to survive. You can help to provide them with food and shelter.

Try to grow flowers that bees and butterflies like. Ask adults for any left-over seeds or save up and buy a packet of mixed wild flower seeds. Other good ones are:

poppies
sunflowers
sweet peas
snapdragons
marigolds
clover
thyme

If you add a small dish of water to your garden (in the shade and surrounded by plants) this can be a home for small amphibians such as frogs, or a bath for the birds.

You can grow a wildlife garden in almost anything. The bees will love the flowers and they will use the nectar to make honey.

This is a supermarket plastic bottle, cut down and planted with tomato pips.

2 HELP YOUR ZOO

Find out what your nearest zoo is doing to help to save animals. Write to them (enclosing a stamped addressed envelope) and ask them about their conservation projects. You might be able to help by adopting an animal.

3 JOIN AN ANIMAL CONSERVATION GROUP

Find a local conservation group and see if they could use your help. You can find addresses at your local library.

They might want help with:
helping toads cross roads
cleaning up a river for the fish
planting trees for the birds and animals

4 DO A PROJECT AT SCHOOL

Ask your teacher if you could do a conservation project at school. You could:

- build a pond
- plant some trees
- make a natural area
- make a butterfly garden

5 DO A PROJECT WITH YOUR FRIENDS

Find an open space near your house that could make a space for wildlife. You could make your own club with badges and membership cards. What about making a wildlife garden in:

- the corner of a churchyard
- a bit of disused land
- the corner of a park

You must ask first! Get adults on your side. They might be able to help.

MAKE A POSTER

You could make a poster for your bedroom wall, or for school, or for a community notice board. Here are some ideas:

ANSWERS

FROM PAGE 14/15

hippopotamus
giraffe
elephant
chimpanzee
antelope
gazelle
python
kangaroo
crocodile

FROM PAGES 18/19

1 The arctic tern. It flies from the arctic (near the north pole) when summer ends there to go to the antarctic (near the south pole) for another summer! This is about 20,000km.

2 The African elephant. Their upper incisor teeth grow as tusks and these can be as long as a car. About 70,000 elephants are killed each year for these valuable ivory tusks. If this goes on there will be no elephants by the start of the 21st century.

3 They have special oil glands near their tails. They put the oil on their fur or feathers and this keeps the water out.

4 The red kangaroo from Australia can jump about 7.5m.

5 The cheetah is the fastest sprinter at 100kmph.

6 Yes, two kinds of mammals lay eggs. The duck-billed platypus lays eggs that have soft and sticky shells and they are laid in a nest in the river bank. The spiny anteater is the other egg-laying mammal. Both of these mammals live in Australia.

7 As dead as a dodo — a large, extinct, flightless bird.

8 Coral

9 Hummingbirds

10 No, they live in Asia.

11 They burrow into the sand and block up the entrance. Their breathing keeps the burrow damp and cool.

12 The mountains of China and Nepal.

CONSERVATION QUIZ

1 The panda

2 2,000

3 Przewalski's horse
Hawaiian goose
Arabian oryx

4 The bison

5 The bald eagle

6 100

7 For the ivory from their tusks

8 The passenger pigeon

9 Whales

10 Crocodiles and alligators

FROM PAGE 27

MAKING TRACKS

1 deer

2 chicken

3 snake

4 fox

5 rabbit

6 duck

7 lion

FROM PAGE 29

(plant eaters)
buffalo
elk
zebra
antelope
elephant
gazelle
sheep
horse
cattle
red deer
springbok
ox
giraffe

(meat eaters)
cheetah
hyena
lion
tiger
jaguar
leopard
cougar
panther
wolf
polar bear

You can read the original story of Noah and the flood in the Bible. It is written in the book of Genesis, beginning in chapter 6.

Designed by The Pinpoint Design Company

Published by
Lion Publishing plc
Sandy Lane West, Oxford, England
ISBN 0 7459 2714 9
Albatross Books Pty Ltd
PO Box 320, Sutherland,
NSW 2232, Australia
ISBN 0 7324 0846 6

First edition 1995

A catalogue record for this book is available from the British Library

Printed and bound in Italy